SINGING, DANCING CARPENTER

Cantata/ Mini Musical Edition

Text and lyrics by Michael Forster
Music by Christopher Tambling

Kevin Mayhew

We hope you enjoy the music in this book. Further copies are available from your local music shop or Christian bookshop.

In case of difficulty, please contact the publisher direct by writing to:

The Sales Department
KEVIN MAYHEW LTD
Rattlesden
Bury St Edmunds
Suffolk
IP30 0SZ

Phone 01449 737978
Fax 01449 737834

Please ask for our complete catalogue of outstanding Church Music.

First published in Great Britain in 1996 by Kevin Mayhew Ltd

ISBN 0 86209 823 8
Catalogue No: 1450049

Front cover illustration by Roy Mitchell.
Cover design by Graham Johnstone and Veronica Ward.

Music Editor: Donald Thomson
Music setting by Tracy Cracknell

Printed and bound in Great Britain

Contents

Foreword

This shortened 'cantata version' has been produced in order to allow *Singing, Dancing Carpenter* to be performed in settings where a two hour stage performance would not be appropriate. The essence of the work remains: it is at once a celebration of life in all its fullness and a protest against all that is life-denying in our lives and the world.

The focus of the work, of course, is Jesus, and the title reflects two things about him which were, according to people's differing points of view, extremely attractive or highly offensive: his festive lifestyle and his comparatively humble station in society. Life, for him, was to be enjoyed and celebrated, and he was particularly concerned to include in the party those whom society was careful not to invite. His opposition to everything which made life unnecessarily burdensome, especially guilt, prejudice and injustice, made him a threat to those who had a vested interest in all that. This cantata highlights the acclamation and the opposition which Jesus encountered, and also reflects upon how easily the one can become the other.

The challenge to us all, in our present age, is to celebrate the goodness of life and to oppose anything which denies it, and this means a particular concern for those who are most disadvantaged. This may also involve a call to confront the structural injustices which exist within the political systems of our own and other nations, for if God cares about the poor then he must surely care about the causes of their poverty. We hope that this cantata will be in itself both a celebration of life – and enjoyable simply as that – and a way of enabling us all to renew our commitment to the marginalised in our own and other societies, not as a duty but as a joy. For this reason, the participation of the congregation is of the utmost importance. Not only do we have the opportunity to make that commitment; we also may be enabled to recognise within ourselves those elements which opposed Jesus and, in good humour, to deal with them!

We are immensely grateful to many churches and other organisations, who have produced the original version of *Singing, Dancing Carpenter* both for the creative imagination which they have brought to bear upon it giving a distinctive slant to each individual performance, and for writing and telling us about it. We have been very much encouraged by this, both in the adaptation of other versions of this work and also in the writing of new ones.

As with the original version, we offer this cantata in the hope that it will be not only thought-provoking and evangelistic (in the best sense of the word) but fun!

MICHAEL FORSTER
CHRISTOPHER TAMBLING.

SINGING, DANCING CARPENTER

Text: Michael Forster (*b.*1946)
Music: Christopher Tambling (*b.*1964)

As the cantata begins, Narrator 2 is seated anonymously in the congregation.

Narrator 1   This is the story of Jesus.

Narrator 2   Oh, I might have known - whenever you come within fifty yards of a church, someone wants to talk about religion!

Narrator 1   Alright, then. This is the story of a singing, dancing carpenter. He was, in many ways, quite an ordinary chap - came from an ordinary home - pursued an ordinary trade. . .

Narrator 2   Well, why are you bothering to tell us about him, then?

Narrator 1   *[Very patiently]* Because he did some extraordinary things.

Narrator 2   *[Approaching front]* And is there any danger that you might actually get on with it, and describe some of them?

Narrator 1   No

Narrator 2   *[Thoroughly exasperated]* Then what's this all about?

Narrator 1   I'm going to let the people whose lives he changed tell the story.

1 SINGING, DANCING CARPENTER (1)

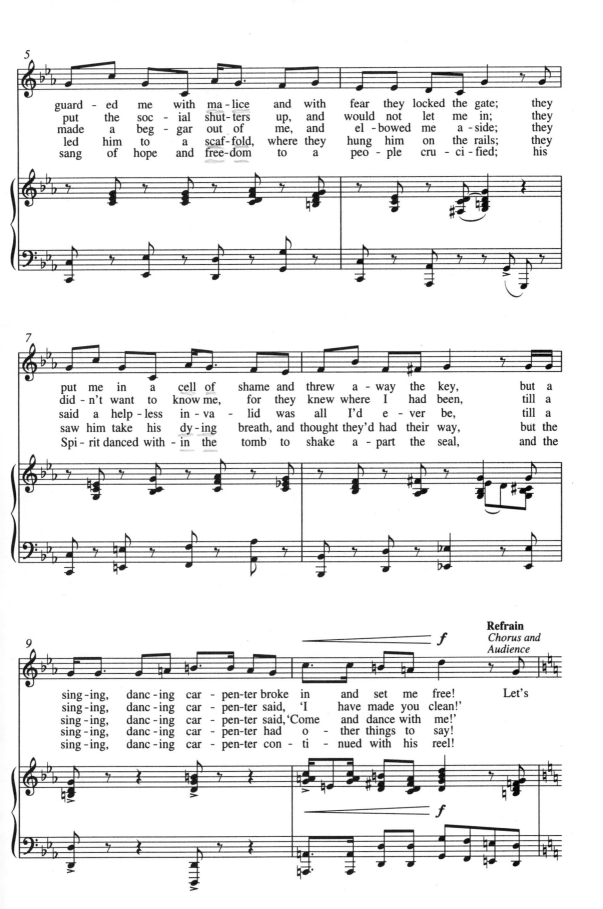

sing with the car - pen - ter a song of li - ber - ty; let's

dance with the car - pen - ter, for all the world to see; let's

learn with the car - pen - ter what God would have us be, and

la - bour with the car - pen - ter to set cre - a - tion

To verses

after v 5. next page

free!

Male Solo 2. They
Male Solo 3. They
Mary Magdalene 4. They
Mary Magdalene 5. He

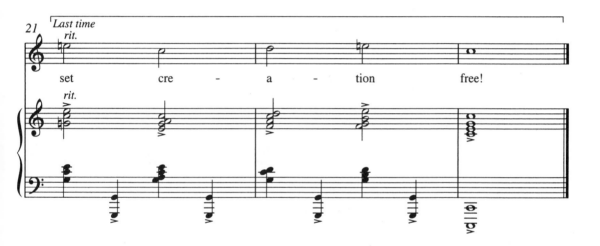

Last time

set   cre - a - tion   free!

Narrator 2	Well, it's a nice story, but when it comes down to it, he's still a religious figure – and that means he's there for the respectable people.
Narrator 1	I wouldn't say that. He mixed with a pretty disreputable lot, really. Take Zacchaeus, for example – he was a tax collector.
Narrator 2	Hey, be careful! You can't go calling tax officials disreputable – there may be some here.
Narrator 1	Well, I think they're a bit different now. For one thing, in Jesus' time Palestine was part of the Roman Empire. So tax collectors were regarded as traitors. And on top of that, they were widely thought to be dishonest; they often overtaxed people and pocketed the difference.
Narrator 2	So, this Zacchaeus was a pretty unpopular fellow.
Narrator 1	You can say that again!

2 OH! ZACCHAEUS!

tax us out of house and home, and ne - ver send it
on to Rome; why don't you tax our ve-ry breath, and charge us du - ty
on our death? Oh! Zac-chae - us! Oh!
Zac-chae - us!

Accusers {
1. He tax-es our live-stock, he
2. He tax-es our wa - ter, he
3. What- e - ver we own or what-

mf

tax - es our crops,   he tax - es the clothes that we   wear;   he
tax - es our oil,   he tax - es the fur - rows we   plough,   he
e - ver we use,   what - e - ver we earn   or we   buy,   what-

tax - es our hou - ses,   he tax - es our food,   and al - ways takes more than his
tax - es our chic - kens,   he tax - es our eggs,   he tax - es the far - row-ing
e - ver we give   and what - e - ver we get   pro - du - ces a gleam in his

f

share.   *Zacchaeus* { I'm do - ing a job   just like ev - 'ry - one else,   and I
sow.   *Zacchaeus* { It's true that I'm tho - rough, but make no mis - take,   I
eye!   *Accusers* If we live in them, walk   on them, buy them or sell,   if we

f

on - ly de - duct what I   must,   but it's hard to be fair   in the
try to be ut - ter - ly   fair.   Why, e - ven my mo - ther, who's
eat them or ride   on their   backs,   if we sleep on them, write with them,

Refrain

world of to-day, when you're earn-ing a dis-hon-est crust. *Chorus* Oh!
se - ven-ty - five is made to-con - tri - bute her share!
like it or not, Zac-chae-us willmake us pay tax!

Za - chae - us! Who will you cheat to-day? Oh! Zac-chae-us! D'you know what

peo - ple say? You charge us tax on ev-'ry - thing, but

you your - self don't pay a thing; you tax us out of

house and home, and ne – ver send it on to Rome;

why don't you tax our ve – ry breath, and charge us du – ty

Getting more and more angry

on our death? Oh! Zac – chae – us! Oh!

Zac – chae – us! Oh! Zac – chae – us!

Shouted

cresc.

ff

Narrator 2	I bet Jesus had a thing or two to say to *that* man!
Narrator 1	Well, Zacchaeus *was* a tax collector, but I don't think they had V.A.T. in those days. . .
Narrator 2	Wake up! I said *that* man, not *VAT* man.
Narrator 1	Sorry. Well, anyway, the point is that Jesus had a special concern for the people who were hated or feared by society – like the woman who touched the edge of his coat one day.
Narrator 2	Why did she do that?
Narrator 1	She needed help, but was too ashamed to face Jesus.
Narrator 2	Well, nothing changes, does it? Some of the religious people I know could make a saint feel guilty.
Narrator 1	I'd like to disagree with you, but I'm afraid there do seem to be a lot of people who think they're not good enough for the church. So they just hang around the edges – rather the way she did.

3 COME AS YOU ARE

'Anna' (a sick woman) 1.The

1. one   who could   heal me I   dare not   ap - proach,   for the
2. hear   peo -ple   talk of the   peace of   the   Lord,   and we'd
3. not   in the   bread and the wine may   we   share,   with our

fear   and the   guilt that I'm bear - ing,   but
like,   if we   could, to re   - ceive it;   but the
guilt   and our   poor un - der - stand - ing,   we'll

such is his power that I'm sure I could be
church is a place for the ho - ly and the
stay at the back, and give place to those who

healed by the edge of the gar - ment he's
good, and the gos - pel's for those who be -
know and can do what the gos - pel's de -

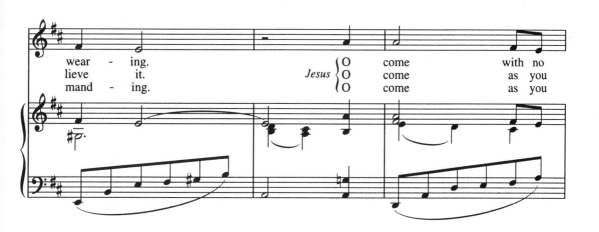

wear - ing.
lieve it. *Jesus* ⎰O come with no
mand - ing. ⎱O come as you
O come as you

fear, look me full in the face; do you
are, with your doubts and your fears, bring-ing
are, to the feast I pre - pare, and be -

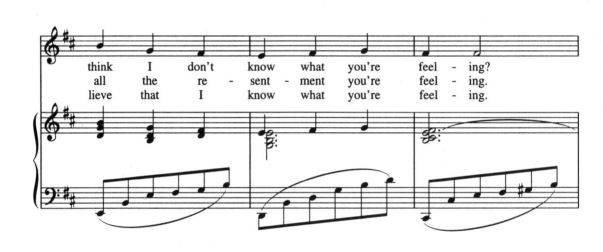

think I don't know what you're feel - ing?
all the re - sent - ment you're feel - ing.
lieve that I know what you're feel - ing.

The love that I have is for
My grace is on of - fer to
For the guests at my ta - ble are

peo - ple just like you, and my on - ly de -
peo - ple just like you, and I've plen - ty of
peo - ple just like you, and my life is poured

sire is your heal - ing!
time for your heal - ing.
out for your heal - ing.

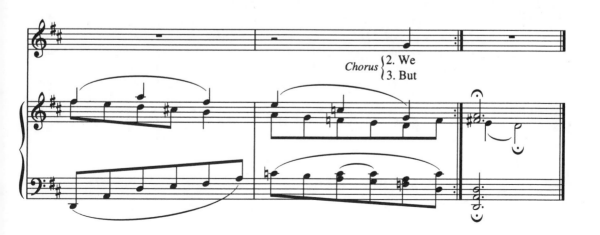

Chorus { 2. We
{ 3. But

Narrator 2	I'm not surprised Jesus upset the religious types – I've always said the church is full of. . .
Narrator 1	The church is full of ordinary people, who have the same fears, prejudices and hang-ups that other ordinary people tend to have.
Narrator 2	So it was the religious establishment that wanted to get rid of Jesus?
Narrator 1	They didn't like him, of course, because they were a privileged group and didn't want the political boat rocking. But there were others.
Narrator 2	Such as who?
Narrator 1	Well, the freedom fighters didn't like him because they wanted a revolution and Jesus preached non-violence; the lawyers didn't like him because they thought he was encouraging anarchy; and they managed to portray him as a threat to law and order so that the government turned against him as well.
Narrator 2	So they ended up with an unholy alliance between four groups of people who in any other circumstances couldn't stand the sight of one another?
Narrator 1	Yes, human behaviour doesn't change much, does it?

4 SINGING, DANCING CARPENTER (2)

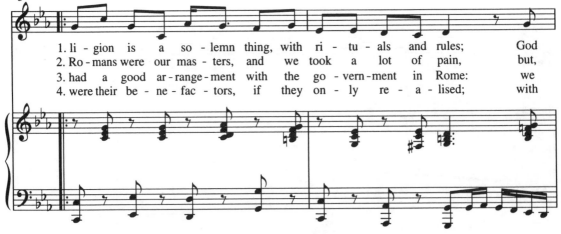

5

on - ly loves the ho - ly, and he's got no time for fools! As
come the re - vo - lu - tion, we'd have had them out a - gain. We
kept God out of po - li - tics; they left our faith a - lone. But
Ro - man peace and Ro - man roads, we made them ci - vi - lised. Yet,

7

guar - dians of the truth, we kept the peo - ple in their place, till a
nee - ded a Mes - si - ah of a fierce and war - like kind; was a
Je - sus threa - tened all of that, and peo - ple could not see that a
ne - ver were they sa - tis - fied; we gave them ev - 'ry - thing, but a

Refrain
Chorus and
Audience

f

9

sing-ing, danc-ing car - pen - ter came preach - ing love and grace. We'll
sing-ing, danc-ing car - pen - ter the best that God could find?
sing-ing, danc-ing car - pen - ter was all he'd e - ver be.
sing-ing, danc-ing car - pen - ter they wan - ted for their king!

f

21

si - lence the car - pen - ter; for once we all a - gree! We'll

ri - di - cule the car - pen - ter for ev' - ry - one to see. We'll

say that the car - pen - ter's not all he claims to be; we'll

To verses

cru - ci - fy the car - pen - ter, and then we'll all be

free!

Zealot 2. The
Priest 3. We
Roman Official 4. We

Last time

then   we'll   all   be   free!

Narrator 2	So how did they go about doing all that?
Narrator 1	Well, they tried various ways of discrediting him, none of which worked, and then Jesus went too far by riding into the city on a donkey.
Narrator 2	Why did he do that?
Narrator 1	It seems he was pointing people back to Zechariah's prophecy about a king entering Jerusalem on a donkey.
Narrator 2	So he was being provocative – trying to start something.
Narrator 1	That's obviously what a lot of people thought, but he was more probably trying to make the point about the sovereignty of love – and people misunderstood him.
Narrator 2	So what happened?
Narrator 1	They gave him a conquering hero's welcome, to begin with. . .

5 CRY HOSANNA!

16 Cry ho - san - na! Cry ho - san - na! Bles - sed

21 be the Ho - ly One! Bles - sed be the

26 **Refrain** *ff* *Chorus* Ho - ly One! Cry ho - san - na! Cry ho -

ff

31 san - na! Wel-come Da - vid's roy - al son!

Cry ho - san - na! Cry ho - san - na! Bles-sed

be the Ho - ly One! Bles - sed be the

Ho - ly One! *Solo* See him rid - ing to the

ci - ty, as the scrip - tures have fore - told;

he will drive the Ro - mans back in - to the sea! We shall see the great ful - fil - ment of the pro - phe - cies un - fold, as all of A - bram's chil - dren are set free!

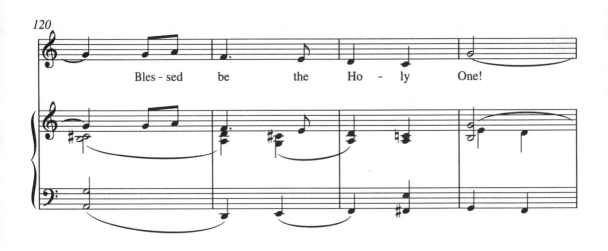

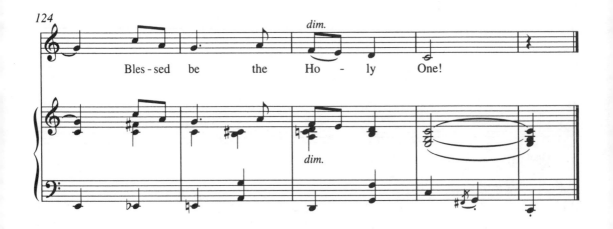

Narrator 2   Well! That lasted about as long as a chocolate frying pan!
Narrator 1   That's how it is with cheap popularity – but it got worse.

6 CRUCIFY HIM!

fy him! Si-lence him for good and all!

Si-lence him for good and all! *Chorus* Cru-ci-

fy him! Cru-ci-fy him! Take him out be-

yond the wall. Cru-ci-fy him! Cru-ci-

Refrain *ff*

fy him! Si-lence him for good and all!

Si-lence him for good and all!

Solo I was on-ly sell-ing lambs and goats for sa - cri-

fi - cial rites, so that peo - ple can ob -

serve the pro - per feast, when this fel - low with a whip came in and put them all to flight, and I lost the price of ev - 'ry sin - gle beast! *Chorus* Cru - ci - fy him! Cru - ci -

Refrain *ff*

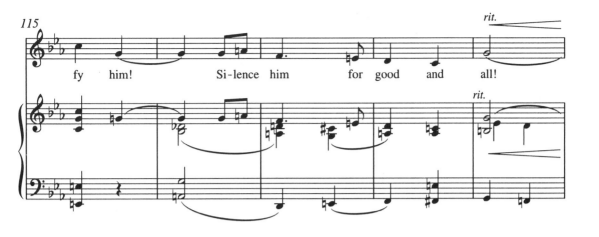

fy   him!   Si-lence him   for   good   and   all!

Si-lence   him   for   good   and   all!

Narrator 2	Things don't change much, do they?
Narrator 1	In what way?
Narrator 2	Hypocrisy – good people get crucified and bad people get religion.
Narrator 1	That's a bit oversimplified, although there's some truth in it, but Jesus showed us how to meet evil with good and overcome it.
Narrator 2	Oh yes – a nice theory – but it didn't help him, did it? You've got to meet force with force in this world.
Narrator 1	You mean overcome evil with evil. But all that does is add to it. Jesus could have fought, and it would just have ended up with a lot more people being killed. He decided that the evil had to stop there.
Narrator 2	So he just let them kill him?
Narrator 1	No – he offered himself as a sacrifice – he willingly gave up his own life to prevent the evil from growing.
Narrator 2	But what good did that do?
Narrator 1	If he'd used evil to fight evil then he'd have discredited all of his own teaching and lost everything. Because he refused to give in to the pressure, he won. But he left a lot of people with more questions than answers.

7 WHAT KIND OF MAN WAS THIS?

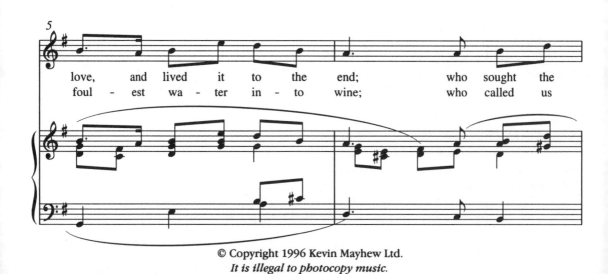

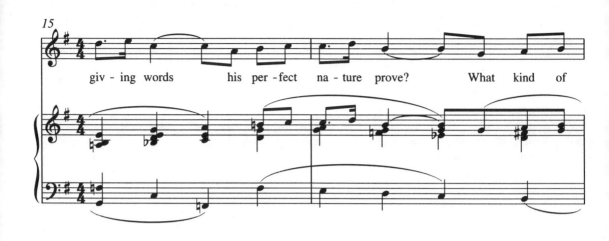

giv - ing words his per - fect na - ture prove? What kind of

man was this, what kind of love? 4. What kind of

Voices or instrument

Ah, ah,

man was this who helped us all to see the full - ness

Narrator 1	The body of Jesus was taken down from the cross and put in a stone tomb, which was sealed up and guarded by soldiers.
Narrator 2	It must have been a dreadful time for the disciples.
Narrator 1	Two days and nights without hope; without relief from the pain of bereavement and failure; the longest two nights of their lives, until. . .
Narrator 2	Until what?
Narrator 1	Suddenly the women came to where the men were hiding and started shouting about Jesus being alive. The men didn't believe a word of it – they probably thought it was an old wives' tale.
Narrator 2	Yes, and I bet *that's* an expression men invented as well!

8 HE'S ALIVE!

Mary Magdalene He's a-

live, he's a-live! He is ri-sen from the dead. He's a-live, he's a-live, yes, a-

live! He's a-live, he's a-live, he is ri-sen from the dead.

That's what the an - gels said, that's what the an - gels

Refrain *f*

said. *Chorus* He's a - live, he's a-live! He is ri-sen from the dead. He's a -

live, he's a-live, yes a - live! He's a - live, he's a - live, he is

ri-sen from the dead. That's what the an - gels said, ah,

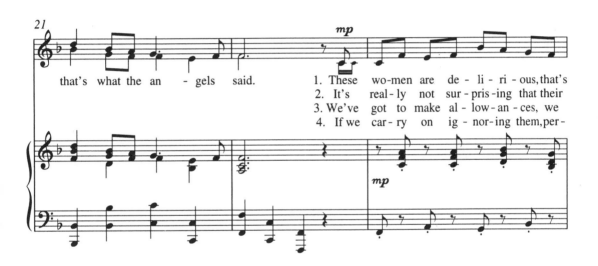

that's what the an - gels said.

1. These wo-men are de - li - ri - ous, that's
2. It's real-ly not sur-pris-ing that their
3. We've got to make al - low-an - ces, we
4. If we car-ry on ig - nor-ing them, per-

all there is to say, their heads are full of gos - sip, fad and
minds are in a mess, they're vic - tims of their own i - ma - gi -
must - n't be un - kind, the last few days have left their sen - ses
haps they'll go a - way. We've said be - fore, and we shall say a -

26

fa - ble!
na - tions.
reel - ing!
gain:

They ne - ver could be se - ri - ous, it's
If we've told them once, we've told them fif - ty
E - vents like these are far too much for
If God had a - ny - thing of such sig -

28

sim - ply not their way,
thou-sand times, not less,
a - ny wo - man's mind,
ni - fi - cance to say,

they're na - tu - ral - ly fligh - ty and un -
to curb their in - fan-tile ex - ag - ge -
we've got to un - der-stand the way they're
he'd have said it to some le - vel - hea - ded

30

Refrain *f*

sta - ble!
ra - tion!
feel - ing!
men!

He's a - live, he's a-live! He is ri - sen from the dead. He's a-

f

live, he's a-live, yes, a-live! He's a-live, he's a-live, he is

ri-sen from the dead. That's what the an - gels said, ah,

that's what the an - gels said. 5. It's ve - ry hard to say it, but they're

that's what the an - gels said. 5. It's ve - ry hard to

clear - ly full of wine — we're sure that they be - lieve this fa - bri -

say it, but they're clear - ly full of wine — we're sure that they be -

ca - tion. They have no in - ner di - sci - pline to

lieve this fa - bri - ca - tion. They have no in - ner

(Stunned silence)

help them draw the line, and drink - ing al - ways means. . .

(Stunned silence)

di - sci - pline to help them draw the line, and drink - ing al - ways means. . .

ri - sen from the dead. That's what we've al - ways

said, ah, that's what we've al - ways

To repeat

said.

Last time

He's a - said.

rit.

dim.

L.H.

pp

Ped.

Narrator 2	They've got a nerve!
Narrator 1	Who have?
Narrator 2	Those men – 'That's what we've always said,' indeed!
Narrator 1	Yes, you're right. The bible makes it quite clear that women were the first to believe and proclaim resurrection, but it also shows how the men very quickly started acting as though it had been them.
Narrator 2	So nothing's changed, then. Religion's still a bastion of privilege and prejudice!
Narrator 1	If you mean God hasn't forced us all suddenly to become perfect, you're right, but we've been given a new opportunity. And there are clear signs in the bible that some attitudes began to change. Jesus made it clear that this was the start of *new* life – not just another helping of the old.
Narrator 2	Where does he say that?
Narrator 1	D'you remember the story about how Jesus met Mary Magdalene in the garden just after the resurrection?

9 DO NOT TOUCH

Gently

Mary Magdalene 1. I

met him in the gar - den   in the ear - ly mor - ning   light,   but I
wan - ted to hold on   to   things the way they were   be - fore,   but he
ri - sen, and he's with   us   in a   form we can - not   grasp,   and with

thought   he was the man   who worked the land,   'till I
said   that was - n't how   it ought to   be.   The
life   the u - ni - verse   can - not con - tain.   And

heard him call me 'Ma - ry' in his own fa - mi - liar
past is now the past, and there are bet - ter things in
not with nails or doc - trines, or a mul - ti - tude of

way, and I saw the wound still o - pen in his
store, and that is why his spi - rit must be
words, will peo - ple e - ver pin him down a -

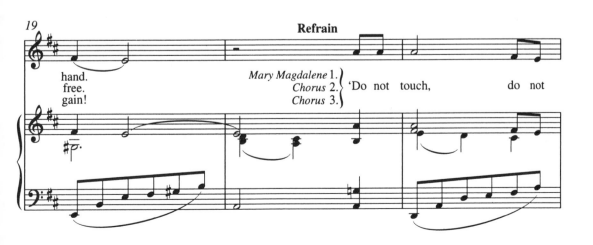

Refrain

hand.
free.
gain!

Mary Magdalene 1.
Chorus 2.
Chorus 3.

'Do not touch, do not

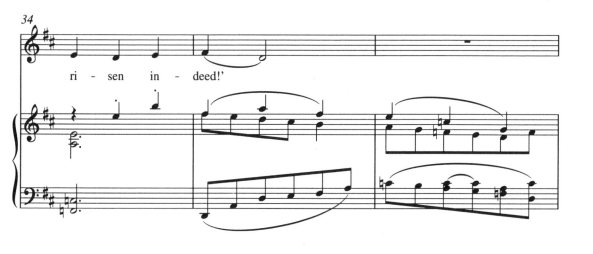

ri - sen in - deed!'

Mary Magdalene {2. I / 3. He's

Narrator 2 Okay, so the fairytale has a happy ending – big deal!

Narrator 1 Oh, there's much more to it than that. People learnt a lot from it. Lives were changed. Take xenophobia, for example.

Narrator 2 Who does he play for?

Narrator 1 Xenophobia – fear of foreigners. Jesus didn't have much time for it.

Narrator 2 So what?

Narrator 1 I imagine you've heard the expression 'There's plenty of fish in the sea'?

Narrator 2 You're not going to tell me that it's an old Jewish proverb?

Narrator 1 I wouldn't know, but the Jewish people of that time believed that there were exactly one hundred and fifty-three different species of fish.

Narrator 2 You're a mine of irrelevant information, aren't you?

Narrator 1 Not entirely irrelevant. There's a story about Jesus meeting his disciples and helping them to catch a remarkable number of fish. I don't suppose you could hazard a guess at how many?

10 ONE HUNDRED AND FIFTY-THREE!

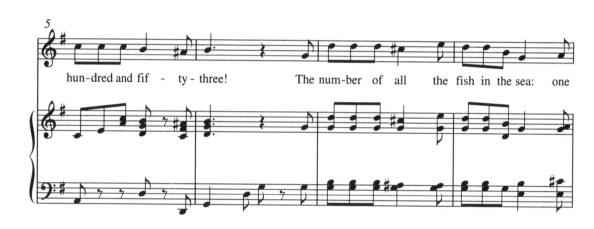

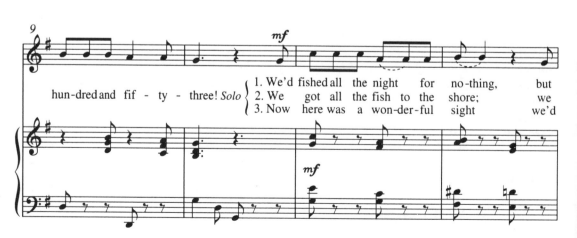

Je - sus said 'Try once more.' So we doubt - ful - ly tried on the
won - dered how ma - ny there'd be. We star - ted to count, and
ne - ver ex - pec - ted to see. And the net did - n't break; it was

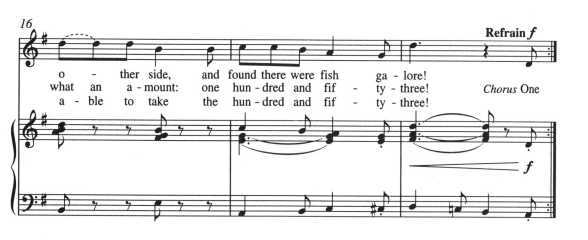

Refrain *f*

o - ther side, and found there were fish ga - lore!
what an a - mount: one hun - dred and fif - ty - three! *Chorus* One
a - ble to take the hun - dred and fif - ty - three!

hun - dred and fif - ty - three! One hun - dred and fif - ty -

three! The num - ber of all the fish in the sea: one

hun - dred and fif - ty - three! *Solo* 4. So, whe - ther you're rich or you're

poor, what - e - ver your race or your sect, be you black, white or brown, Je - sus

wants you a - round; there's plen - ty of room in the net! *Chorus* One hun - dred and fif - ty -

three! One hun-dred and fif - ty - three! The num-ber of all the

fish in the sea: one hun-dred and fif - ty three! One hun dred and fif - ty -

three! One hun-dred and fif - ty - three! The num-ber of all the

Slowly

Tempo I

fish in the sea: one hun-dred and fif - ty - three!

Narrator 2	Yes, well this is all very nice, but the world's still a pretty hopeless place.
Narrator 1	Oh, I don't think so. There's still a lot of hope – but we need to do our part.
Narrator 2	Yes, yes, yes, I know - give your heart to Jesus and you'll have pie in the sky when you die. Some of us don't want to be fobbed off with jam tomorrow – we'd like to see a few more people getting bread today.
Narrator 1	Then let's go and look for Jesus.
Narrator 2	Oh, right – sitting on a cloud somewhere – fat lot of use he is there.
Narrator 1	No, in this world, where he told us to look – among the people he chose to spend his time with before – like the homeless, the unwanted, the sick – *[Turns to choir]* Come on, you lot, give me a hand. Tell him / her where *you* have found him.

11 SINGING, DANCING CARPENTER (3)

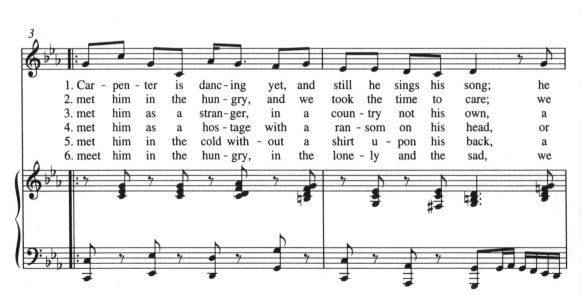

sing with the car - pen - ter till peace and jus - tice spread; let's

dance with the car - pen-ter and fol - low where he's led; let's

sing and dance for free - dom, see the poor and hun-gry fed, pro -

To verses

claim - ing that the car - pen - ter is ri - sen from the

dead!

Solo { 2. We
3. We
4. We
5. We
6. We

ri - sen from the dead!

Last time